The Little Lamb
of
Bethlehem

Words & Pictures by
Margaret Tempest

London. The Medici Society Ltd.

The Little Lamb

ONCE upon a time, many years ago, a little lamb was born in the country of Judea.

The little lamb had no brothers or sisters, and though he often played with the other lambs in the field, he sometimes liked to go for walks by himself. He made friends with the little beasts of the field, the rabbits and mice and the birds.

SOMETIMES in the night he would leave his mother's warm side and go out alone in the dark. He did not fear the owls and the foxes: for they knew him and did him no harm.

NEAR the field where the lamb was born stood a small town and often the lamb looked at the town and wished he could go to it. Most of all he wished this on winter evenings when the lights of the little town twinkled through the dark, but he dared not go. He was afraid of the people in the town, for the only people he knew were the shepherds who tended the flock.

ONE cold winter night the little lamb felt that he must go and look at the lights of the town. He crept away very quietly, so as not to disturb his mother, who was sleeping, and very quietly he walked to the end of the field nearest to the town.

THE little lamb saw that a new light was shining among the houses — a light he had never seen before.

It seemed to come from an open doorway and he longed to go and look in at the door. He had a feeling that some wonderful thing was happening there.

AND suddenly an Angel of the Lord appeared in the sky, and the Glory of the Lord shone round about him.

And the Angel said, "Fear not, for, behold, I bring you good tidings of great joy. For unto you is born this day in the city of David, a Saviour which is Christ the Lord. And this shall be a sign unto you. Ye shall find the babe in swaddling clothes, lying in a manger."

AND suddenly there was with the Angel, a multitude of the Heavenly Host, praising God and saying, "Glory to God in the Highest, and on earth peace, goodwill toward men."

When the Angels had gone, the little lamb knew that the light in the doorway showed the birthplace of the baby Christ, and that he must go to Him.

He found his way to the door of the stable and peeped in.

THERE he saw the baby, Jesus
Christ, lying in a manger, and
a small strange light shone round
about Him.

A lovely gentle lady who was
Mary, Jesus' Mother, sat beside
Him, and by her was Joseph, a big
kind man, whom God had chosen
to care for Mary and the baby.

MARY saw the little lamb peeping round the door, and she smiled at him and nodded, to show that he might come and see her baby.

The baby lifted his hand and crooned at the little lamb as if in blessing, and the little lamb knew that he would always love the baby Jesus, and wished that he could stay with Him for ever.

HE thought that he would guard the baby in the night, and he curled up under the manger. Soon he heard the sounds of footsteps outside and of muddy sandals being taken off, and he saw three Shepherds standing at the door.

MARY held out her hand to the shepherds to beckon them in, and they came very gently on tip-toe to the manger. The baby Jesus lifted his hand and crooned to them, as if in blessing, and they knelt and worshipped Him.

THE little lamb stayed very still under the manger for fear that the shepherds should find him and take him away.

When the shepherds had gone Mary lay down to sleep on the clean straw of the stable, and Joseph covered her with her long blue cloak. Joseph slept too, but the little lamb watched and listened all night.

HE knew that Mary and Joseph and the baby would go to their own home, and that it was too far for a little lamb to go and he must return to his mother.

When it began to get light, for the day was coming, he said goodbye to the sleeping baby Jesus, and went very quietly out of the stable.

AS he went on his way he saw some small birds sitting on a branch. "Little lamb, where have you been so early in the day?" said they.

The lamb told them about the Angels and the baby Jesus in the manger, and the birds all started to sing "Glory to God in the Highest."

"THIS is news for all the world" said the Robin, "We will tell our friends and they will tell all the other birds, and the birds will tell everyone in the world that Christ is born to-day."

When we hear the birds singing in the trees perhaps they are still saying "Glory to God in the Highest," and telling us of the birth of Jesus Christ in the stable at Bethlehem.

Printed in England   THE MEDICI PRESS   Ref. 534
First Published 1957

SBN 85503023 2